LOCK

Ballads
Accordion Songbook

Wise Publications
London/New York/Paris/Sydney/Copenhagen/Madrid

Exclusive Distributors:

Music Sales Limited
8/9 Frith Street,
London W1V 5TZ, England.

Music Sales Pty Limited
120 Rothschild Avenue,
Rosebery, NSW 2018,
Australia.

Order No. AM951082
ISBN 0-7119-7092-0
This book © Copyright 1998 by Wise Publications

Book design by Chloë Alexander
Compiled by Peter Evans
Music arranged by Pete Lee
Music processed by Enigma Music Production Services

Printed in the United Kingdom by
Printwise (Haverhill) Limited, Haverhill, Suffolk.

Cover photography by George Taylor
Instrument featured: Trevani Francesco, made in Castelfidardo, Italy
by Guerrini & Figli. Kindly loaned by Trevani, 14 Mapledale Avenue,
Croydon CR0 5TB, England.
Cover photograph: Mariah Carey.

Your Guarantee of Quality
As publishers, we strive to produce every book to the highest commercial standards.
The music has been freshly engraved and the book has been carefully designed to minimise
awkward page turns and to make playing from it a real pleasure.
Particular care has been given to specifying acid-free, neutral-sized paper made from pulps
which have not been elemental chlorine bleached. This pulp is from farmed sustainable
forests and was produced with special regard for the environment.
Throughout, the printing and binding have been planned to ensure a sturdy, attractive
publication which should give years of enjoyment.
If your copy fails to meet our high standards, please inform us and we will gladly replace it.

Music Sales' complete catalogue describes thousands of titles and is available in full colour
sections by subject, direct from Music Sales Limited. Please state your areas of interest and
send a cheque/postal order for £1.50 for postage to: Music Sales Limited, Newmarket Road,
Bury St. Edmunds, Suffolk IP33 3YB.

Visit the Internet Music Shop at
http://www.musicsales.co.uk

And I Love You So

Words & Music by Don McLean

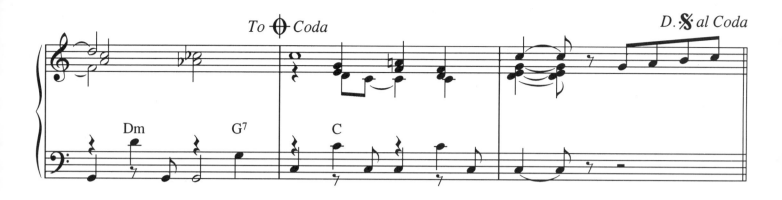

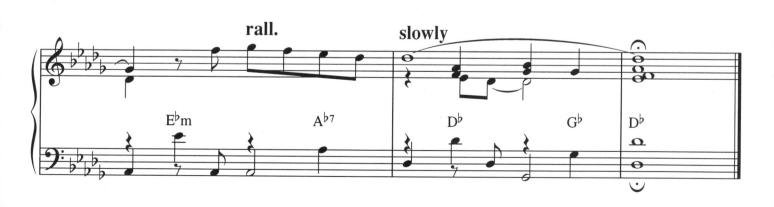

Candle In The Wind

Words & Music by Elton John & Bernie Taupin

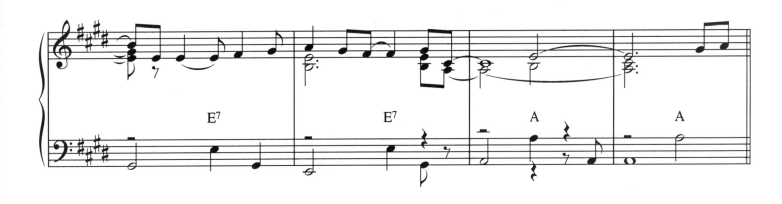

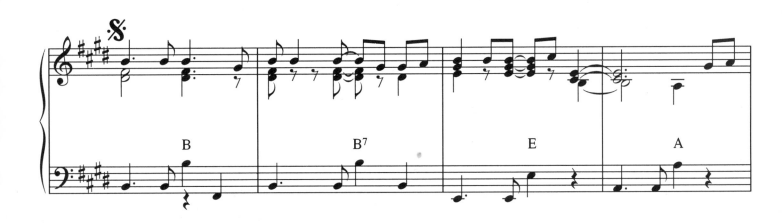

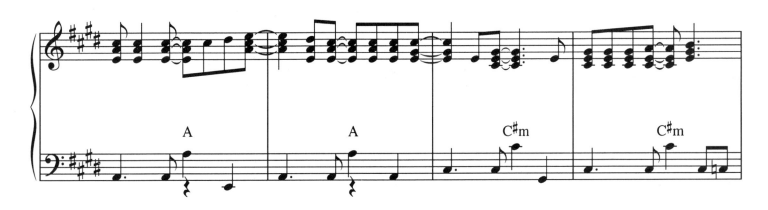

To ⊕ Coda

8

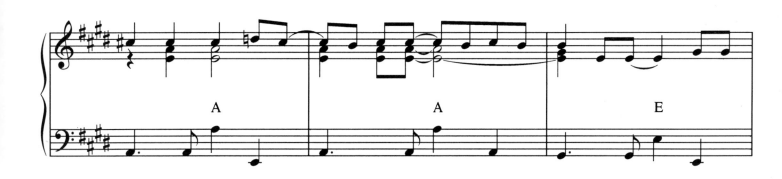

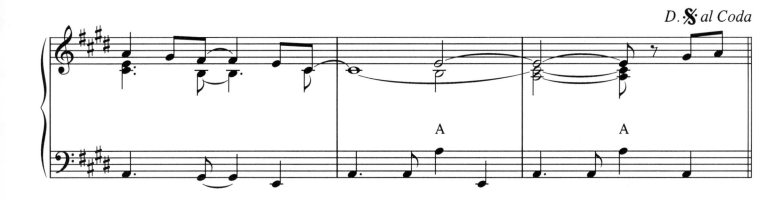

D. %: al Coda

⊕ **CODA**

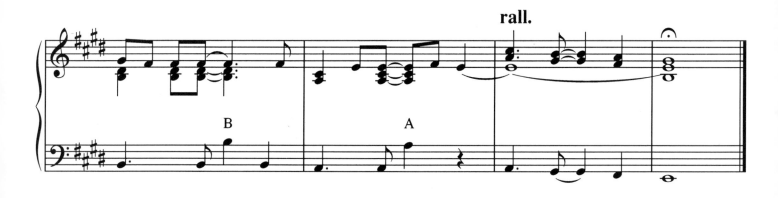

rall.

9

(Everything I Do) I Do It For You

Words by Bryan Adams & Robert John 'Mutt' Lange ◆ Music by Michael Kamen

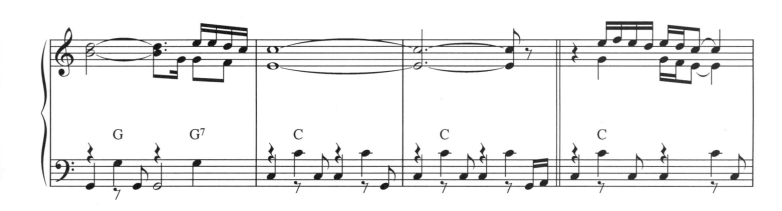

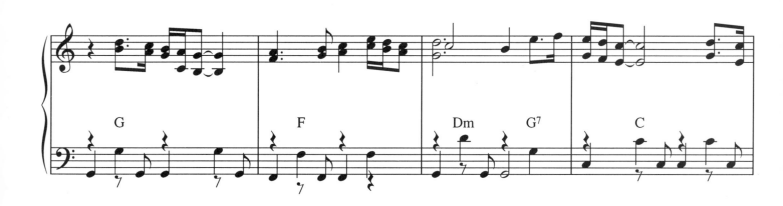

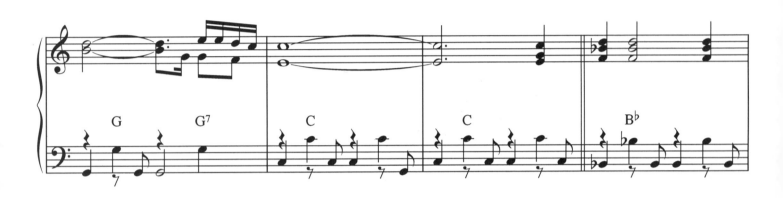

Have I Told You Lately?

Words & Music by Van Morrison

D.S al Coda

Killing Me Softly With His Song

Words by Norman Gimbel ◆ Music by Charles Fox

D.S. al Coda

20

One Moment In Time

Words & Music by Albert Hammond & John Bettis

Moderately slow

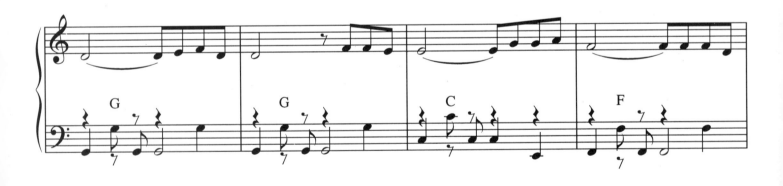

D. %: al Coda

CODA

25

Sometimes When We Touch

Words & Music by Dan Hill & Barry Mann

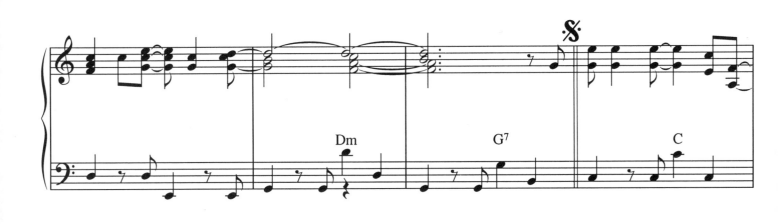

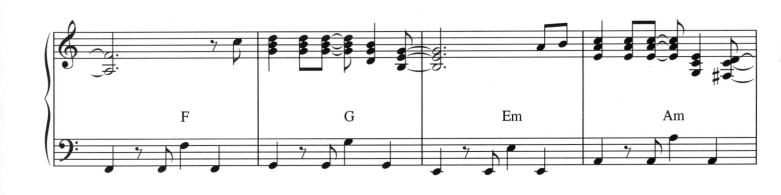

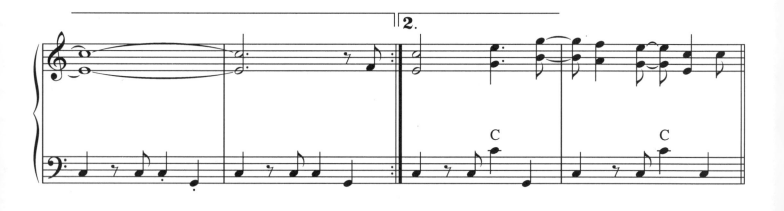

D. 𝄋 al Coda

CODA

rall.

The First Time Ever I Saw Your Face

Words & Music by Ewan MacColl

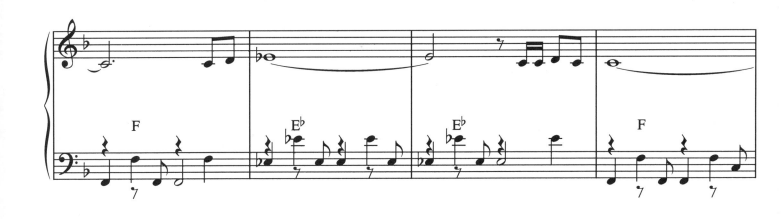

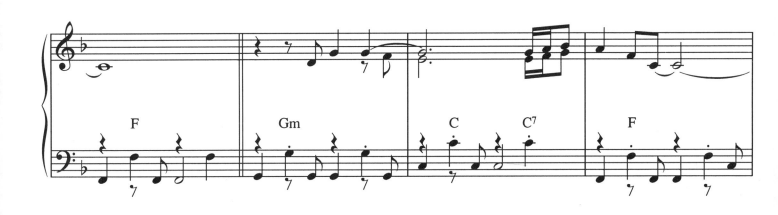

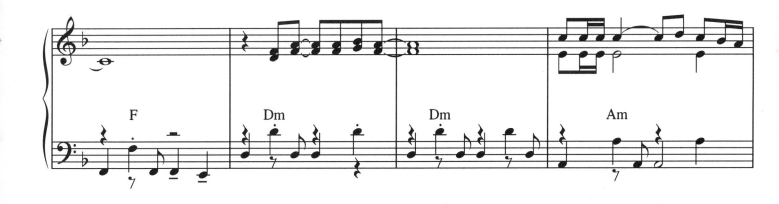

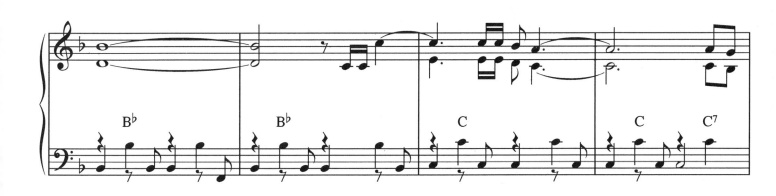

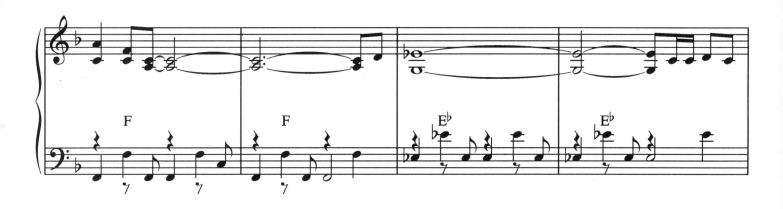

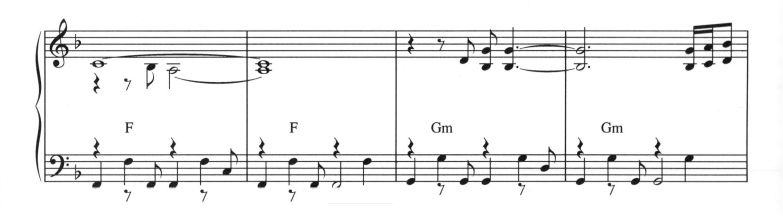

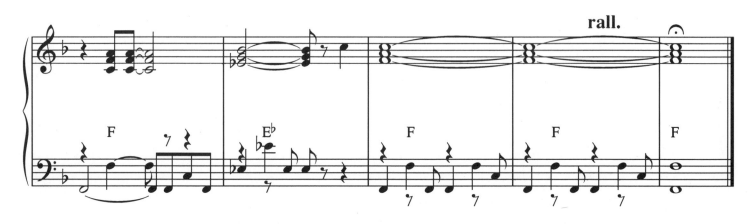

Unchained Melody

Words by Hy Zaret ◆ Music by Alex North

D. %S al Coda

CODA

37

When You Tell Me That You Love Me

Words & Music by Albert Hammond & John Bettis

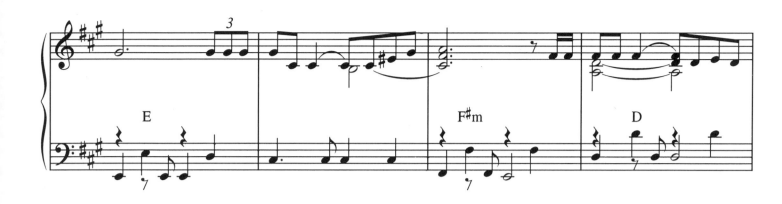

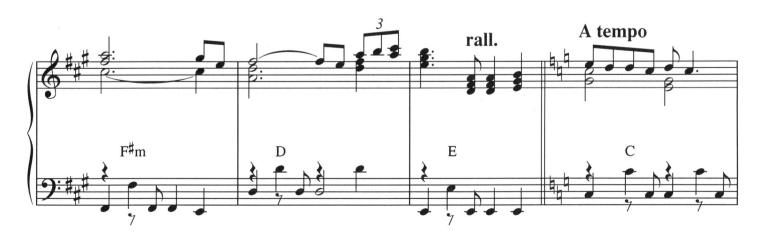

Am   F   Dm   G   G⁷   C

Am   F   Dm   G   G⁷

C   Am   F

molto rall.

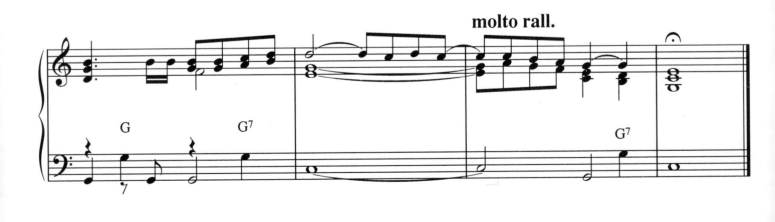

G   G⁷   G⁷

Without You

Words & Music by Peter Ham & Tom Evans

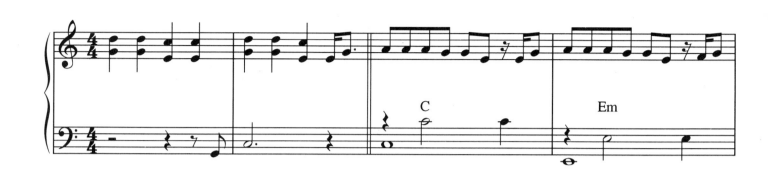

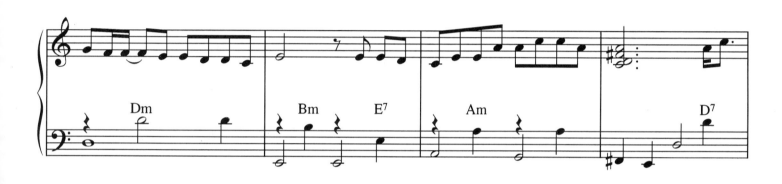

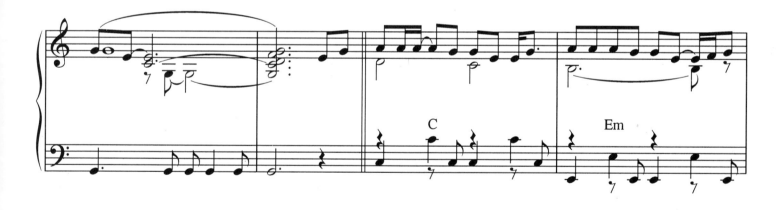

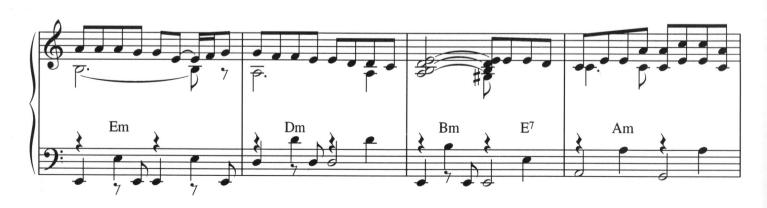

You Must Love Me

Music by Andrew Lloyd Webber ◆ Lyrics by Tim Rice